ثُـچَـارن قيصَـــنبيْ عليهم السَّلام

Yusuf

Abdul Rahman Rukaini

M
MACMILLAN PUBLISHERS

Text © Abdul Rahman Rukaini 1984, English edition 1985.
Illustrations © Macmillan Publishers (M) Sdn. Bhd. 1984, English edition 1985.

Bahasa Malay edition first published 1984.
Published by Macmillan Publishers (M) Sdn. Bhd. co-publication with
Pustaka Pertubuhan Kebajikan Islam Malaysia.

This edition first published 1985

Published by *Macmillan Publishers Ltd*
London and Basingstoke
Associated companies and representatives in Accra,
Auckland, Delhi, Dublin, Gaborone, Hamburg, Harare,
Hong Kong, Kuala Lumpur, Lagos, Manzini, Melbourne,
Mexico City, Nairobi, New York, Singapore, Tokyo

ISBN 0–333–41420–9 (cased)
ISBN 0–333–40018–6 (pbk) ✓
Printed in Hong Kong

Adviser for text:
Ustaz Haji Abu Hassan Din al-Hafiz

Adviser for illustrations:
Abdul Aziz Ibrahim

Designer and artist:
Abdul Razak Abdullah
(ERAL)

British Library Cataloguing in Publication Data
Rukaini, Abdul Rahman
  Stories of the prophets of Islam.
  1. Prophets in the Koran—Biography—Juvenile
  literature
  I. Title
  297′.122′0922   BP134.P745

  ISBN 0–333–41420–9 (cased)
  ISBN 0–333–40018–6 (pbk)

Preface

All the stories in this volume concern the life of the prophet Yusuf; from the time of his strange dream in childhood through to the time when he is eventually re-united with his father, the prophet Ya'qub, after years of living in Egypt.

The strength of the prophet Yusuf's faith is shown clearly by the way in which he forgave his brothers who had abandoned him in a well, and by the way in which he never allowed the praise of his beauty to make him proud.

The stories correspond with the stories of the prophet Yusuf in the Quran. The episodes have been carefully selected and creatively written in order to appeal to young readers.

Illustrations

Contents

Yusuf's dream

Yusuf woke up early that morning. Soft moonlight filled his room and a gentle breeze blew from the open window. Yusuf hugged himself as he lay under the blanket that had belonged to his mother, his head resting on her pillow. He was thinking. He often thought about his mother, Rahil, who had died when his little brother, Binyamin, was born. But this morning he wasn't thinking about her. He wasn't sad. He felt refreshed after his good night's sleep, and happy. Something very special had happened that night. Yusuf had had a dream. He did not know what the dream meant. It was strange, but not frightening. He felt sure it was an important dream although he couldn't understand its message.

He got up and stood at the window. The sun was rising but it was still cool. The clear, full moon, and the stars still twinkled in the sky. They reminded Yusuf of his dream.

'The sun, the moon and the stars', he said to himself, trying to find a meaning. But it was hopeless. He couldn't solve the mystery. There was no point in waking Binyamin. He wouldn't be able to explain the dream either. But Yusuf felt sure that his father, the prophet Ya'qub, would know. Yusuf tiptoed from the room and went to find his father.

The prophet smiled when he saw Yusuf coming towards him.

'Father,' said Yusuf, 'I had a dream last night.'

'A dream?' asked Ya'qub gently as he looked at his son's face.

'Yes, a wonderful dream', said Yusuf.

'Tell me about it', said the prophet, as he sat down with Yusuf.

Carefully Yusuf explained. 'In my dream I saw eleven stars, and the sun and the moon. They bowed down before me! Please tell me what it means, Father. I don't understand the message.'

The prophet hugged his son with joy when he heard his story. Yusuf was surprised. He waited for his father to explain.

'My child,' the prophet began, 'your dream is very important. I have wanted this to happen for a long time.'

'What do you mean, Father?'

asked Yusuf.

'This dream is a sign from Allah. He will give His blessing to you as He did to me, your father, and to my father, Ishaq, and to my father's father, Ibrahim', explained the prophet Ya'qub. 'You will be blessed with goodness and wisdom.'

Yusuf was silent. He did not know what to say. His father sat in silence, too. He watched Yusuf thoughtfully. He was afraid of what might happen if his other sons heard about this dream.

One by one, the prophet Ya'qub thought of each of his children by Laiyah, and by Laiyah's slave and by Rahil's slave. None of them loved Yusuf and Binyamin. They were all envious of the two motherless boys. In his heart Ya'qub prayed to Allah.

'O Allah, protect my child, Yusuf. Save him from harm.'

The prophet warned Yusuf. 'Don't tell your brothers about this dream. They will hate you and envy you even more than they do now. They might try to harm you and your brother Binyamin.'

Yusuf was astonished and sad at his father's words. He did not know his elder brothers hated him so much. But he kissed his father and promised he would keep his dream a secret.

بسم الله الرحمن الرحيم

The plot

Rawbin was the eldest son but he knew he wasn't his father's favourite. He was sure his father loved Yusuf and Binyamin best. The others knew it, too; Syam'un, Lawi, Yahuza, Yasakir, and Zabulun, Dan and Naftali, Jad and Asir, they all knew their father did not love them as much as he loved Rahil's sons.

The jealousy in their hearts grew until Iblis saw his opportunity. He encouraged their hatred and persuaded them to do something wrong. Iblis gave the brothers an idea.

The brothers had something very important to discuss in secret. They met at the foot of a lonely hill. Syam'un looked round before he spoke, to make sure no one else was there.

'We all know that our father loves Yusuf and Binyamin more than he loves us', he complained. 'It isn't fair.'

For a moment the other brothers were silent. As they thought about

the truth of Syam'un's words, their anger and hatred grew.

'I don't understand why Father behaves like this. Yusuf is clearly his favourite, but he is only twelve years old. I am the eldest son', said Rawbin angrily.

'I don't understand either', agreed Yasakir. 'We are older than Yusuf and Binyamin. We are stronger. We are good sons and respect our father.'

'Of course', said Zabulan. 'Why, we even take care of Yusuf and Binyamin.'

'Then why does our father love them more?' They could not answer the question. They knew nothing of Yusuf's dream and Allah's purpose for him.

'Our father is unjust! Unjust!' they cried.

'But we still need our father's love', said Zabulun. 'If we speak like this about him, how can we expect him to love us?' Zabulun did not like speaking against his father. 'We must find a way to make our father love us.'

Yasakir, Jad and the others agreed with him.

'Let's go to him and tell him how we feel', suggested Zabulun. 'We'll ask him for his love.'

Some of the brothers thought this was a good idea but some did not. Both Syam'un and Rawbin were against it.

'Our father's love for Yusuf is too strong', said Syam'un. 'It won't be changed by words.'

'What can we do then?' asked Zabulun.

'As long as Yusuf is with the family, we will be ignored', said Syam'un. 'We have only once choice. We must separate Yusuf from our father.'

The others were amazed at Syam'un's suggestion but no one spoke against it. Encouraged by Iblis, Syam'un went on, 'We could kill Yusuf and hide the evidence of his murder.' The others shuddered at his cruel words. 'Or we could take him to a distant land and leave him to be killed by wild animals. Or we could bury him alive in the desert. Then, when Yusuf has gone, our father's love for us will grow. We can ask Allah's forgiveness for our crime and we will sin no more.'

Yahuza, who had been listening quietly, interrupted at this point. He had a different suggestion.

'We are all the sons of the prophet Ya'qub, from the family of Ibrahim. We know we must not murder, and our religion forbids it. Yusuf has done no wrong. He has not hurt any of us.'

'But how can we make our father forget Yusuf?' cried Rawbin and Yasakir.

'All we need to do,' continued Yahuza, 'is take him to the well of Jub. It's a long way from here. Travellers stop there for water.' The others began to understand his plan.

'What then?' asked one of them.

'We will put Yusuf into the well. If he dies in the well it will not be because we killed him, but because he drowned. And if he is lucky, maybe a traveller will see him and rescue him.'

Even Syam'un agreed. They all knew that if Yusuf was found, he would be sold into slavery and lost forever.

'So we will not be guilty of murder', Yahuza finished.

All the brothers agreed with his plan. It was already evening and the shadows were growing long. It was time to go home. Next day they would go to the prophet Ya'qub and persuade him to let them take Yusuf to play in the hills. There they could carry out their evil plan.

Have pity on me!

It was not easy to persuade Ya'qub to let Yusuf go with them.

'I'm afraid a wolf may catch him', said Ya'qub. 'While you are looking after your goats you may not notice what happens to Yusuf.'

But the brothers promised to be careful to look after Yusuf. They convinced Ya'qub that Yusuf would enjoy playing in the hills, and he would be safe with his ten brothers. So the worried father agreed to let his favourite son go.

Soon hills and trees hid them from the house. The brothers walked faster and faster, hurrying Yusuf along. When no one could see them, Rawbin began to bully Yusuf. He pushed him to make him walk faster and when Yusuf fell, no one helped him up. Yusuf picked himself up and walked on. Then Syam'un pushed him into the sand. He fell heavily, cutting his knee, and picked himself up again. Yusuf's face was white. His brothers frightened him. Rawbin, who was the biggest and strongest, took hold of Yusuf and threw him onto the sand. He pushed Yusuf's face into the sand.

'I'll kill you', he threatened.

'No! Please don't kill me!' cried Yusuf, terrified.

'Dreamer!' Rawbin accused him. 'Tell me what you dreamed about and maybe I'll let you live.'

'I didn't dream anything', Yusuf replied, frightened. He remembered his father's warning that he should keep his dream a secret.

'He's lying!' cried the brothers.

'N – no, I didn't dream anything', lied Yusuf.

Rawbin took Yusuf by the throat. Yusuf screamed for help, but none of the others moved. They all stood round, cheering Rawbin on. Except Yahuza. He could not bear to hear Yusuf's cries. But what could he do against all the others? He gathered all his courage and tried to stop them. He reminded them of the agreement they had made the night before. He told them he had promised his father that he would take care of Yusuf. Meanwhile Yusuf prayed silently to Allah to save him. At last, even Rawbin and Syam'un were persuaded to carry out the original plan.

They dragged Yusuf to the well of Jub. When he saw the well, Yusuf realised what his brothers intended to do. His heart went cold with fear as he thought of the cold, deep water. But how could he escape?

They stripped him of his clothes. He struggled helplessly, begging, 'My brothers, please leave me my clothes!' His voice shook. But his brothers, hearts were hard. They tied Yusuf's hands and let him down into the well.

'My brothers, have mercy, don't leave me in this well. Brothers, have pity on me,' cried Yusuf. His frightened voice echoed in the well. They flung the rope down into the well and left him there.

Now they were satisfied. They were sure that their father would love them now, without Yusuf to take all his attention.

'We've done it!' cried Syam'un.

'Not yet,' said Rawbin. 'We haven't finished yet. We have to make sure our father thinks Yusuf is dead.'

They were all silent, thinking about what to do. Then Iblis spoke into Syam'un's ear, just as once he had whispered to Qabil.

'This is the way', said Syam'un.

'We'll kill a goat and spread its blood on Yusuf's clothes. Then our father will believe that Yusuf has been eaten by a wolf.'

Everyone agreed to the plan and the goat was killed. Syam'un was ready to return home but Rawbin stopped him.

'We should wait until it gets dark,' said Rawbin, 'then our father will believe that we did our best to save Yusuf, but failed. We will go home in tears.'

So they did. But they didn't know that Allah sent the Angel Jibril to put a stone in the well. Yusuf managed to stand on this stone. When he was frightened and in despair, Allah sent him His protection.

Zulaiha in love

Zulaiha had been happy to look after the child her husband bought in the market. But now her feelings had changed. She had forgotten the frightened little boy she had nursed, who had been found in a well and sold as a slave. The child had grown up into a handsome young man, whose beauty had won Zulaiha's heart.

As first she had tried to ignore the feelings she felt for him. She told herself it was just her imagination. She couldn't really be falling in love. But as time went on, the love in her heart grew stronger and she could not pretend she didn't love him.

'Why must I love him?' she cried to herself, 'Why?'

There was no answer. She knew that she was the wife of an important man. She knew it was wrong to feel like this, but she could do nothing about it. His eyes, his lips, his nose, his face, his fingers, even his shadow made her weak with love for him.

She could no longer ignore her feelings. She forgot how she ought to behave. She was desperate for him to love her too.

'I don't care what anybody thinks', she decided. 'I must tell him I love him.' And she called him to her.

'Yusuf', she began softly. Yusuf stood politely in silence.

'How lovely your hair is', said Zulaiha, coming closer to him. Yusuf was embarrassed but Zulaiha went on, 'And how beautiful your eyes and your face are.'

'In the grave they will just be meat for worms,' said Yusuf. He had no interest in worldly beauty.

There was no one in the house and Zulaiha grew more bold. Almost touching him, she said softly, 'Yusuf, we are alone. Why do you hesitate?'

She held her breath but Yusuf said nothing. He looked down at the ground. Zulaiha urged him again.

Firmly Yusuf replied, 'I seek my joy only in Allah. Your husband is a great man here. I honour him. I will not deceive him.' And he left the house.

But Zulaiha became more determined. One day she closed all the doors in the house and tried to force Yusuf. Yusuf had no choice. He turned to run, but Zulaiha caught at his clothes as he fled and they tore at the back. He ran to the door and, flinging it open, ran right into the arms of al-Aziz, Zulaiha's husband. His nephew was with him.

Zulaiha was horrified. Quickly she thought of what to do so she wouldn't be blamed. She ran crying to al-Aziz.

'What is the punishment for someone who tries to take another man's wife?' she asked. But she still loved Yusuf and was afraid he might be sentenced to death, so she added, 'I think it is best to send him to prison or beat him.'

'I would rather go to prison than do what you wanted me to do', said Yusuf.

Al-Aziz was confused, and he turned to his nephew, a learned man, to seek a fair judgement. His nephew pointed to the evidence; Yusuf's clothes were torn at the back, as if he had been running away, not at the front. Both he and his nephew realised Zulaiha was lying.

Al-Aziz thought for a moment, then he said, 'Zulaiha, ask Allah to forgive you for your sin against an innocent man'. Then he smiled at Yusuf. 'Yusuf, forget what has happened and do not tell anyone about it.'

Yusuf left the house with great respect for al-Aziz, and relief.

Forty foolish women

Yusuf kept his promise and told no one what had happened. But somehow people found out about Zulaiha's love for Yusuf and the story spread quickly from person to person.

Soon everyone knew. All the women of the town whispered about it to each other. They all said how dreadful it was that one of their own sex had behaved so badly. Not one of them had a good word to say for Zulaiha. They laughed behind Zulaiha's back and ignored her when they saw her in the town.

'She has brought shame on her family', they said. 'She forgot her duties as the wife of an important man.'

Zulaiha knew what the women were saying about her. She knew that they all laughed at her and she was furious. How could they be so unkind? They did not understand her feelings.

At last she thought of a way to stop their gossip.

'I'll let them see for themselves', she decided.

So she organised a party and invited forty of the most important women in the town. Zulaiha watched her guests as they talked and laughed and ate the wonderful food she had prepared. Then, when all the women were cutting the fruit she had served at the end of the meal, Zulaiha called Yusuf into the room.

Silence fell as they stared at the beautiful man. Zulaiha smiled. She

had been sure that when they saw Yusuf they would feel as she did.

'Yes, this is Yusuf', she said. 'This is the man you have laughed at me for loving.'

No one spoke. The women were still staring unashamedly at Yusuf.

'You have only had a glance at him, but already you are half-mad with love. Think of me. I see him every day. How could I resist his beauty? I admit I fell in love with him.' Then Zulaiha laughed at the women. 'Look at you', she said. 'You are all so stunned by Yusuf that you've cut yourselves on your fruit knives, but you didn't feel the pain.'

Now they all sympathised with Zulaiha, but at her next words they were horrified.

'Because he refused me, I have decided to have him sent to prison.'

They were now all in love with Yusuf themselves and knew he was innocent. They begged Yusuf to grant Zulaiha's wish so that he would not be flung into prison. But Yusuf would not listen to them. Instead he prayed. So Zulaiha went to her husband and demanded that Yusuf must be imprisoned. For the sake of his good name and to prevent more gossip, al-Aziz agreed.

Yusuf accepted his sentence calmly. He chose prison rather than sin.

In the prison

At last Yusuf was free. He was free
from temptation, free from worrying
about Zulaiha's behaviour. He felt
calm and happy. He could think of
Allah every minute of the day and
worship His greatness. Yusuf was
glad to be in prison.

It was the first time that those
stone walls and iron bars had
become a place of worship. The
usual sounds of weeping and despair
gave way to the sound of Yusuf's
voice praising Allah.

Life was not easy in prison, but
Yusuf did not regret what he had
done and never gave up hope. He
always had a smile for the other
prisoners and they were glad to talk
to him. He learnt why each man had
been put in prison. Some were guilty
and some were innocent but they all
needed care and help. He learnt a lot
about men's needs and problems.

Every day Yusuf looked after
those who were ill and comforted
those who had given up hope. He
gave them new courage and taught
them the difference between right
and wrong.

It was in this prison that Yusuf
first heard the word of Allah,

making him Allah's prophet. Allah commanded Yusuf to turn mankind from the ways of cruelty and despair, to show them the way of truth and justice. So Yusuf talked to his fellow prisoners and one by one they began to put their trust in Allah. Soon other voices joined Yusuf's in praising Allah. In that prison miserable men found a new will to live. Their weeping was replaced by prayer.

The other prisoners often came to Yusuf's cell to ask him questions and learn from him. One morning two new prisoners came to see him. They seemed to be frightened and nervous, as if something terrible had happened to them.

'Are you the man who can explain dreams?' asked one of them.

Yusuf smiled and said, yes, Allah had given him that skill.

'Can we ask you a question, sir?'

'Of course', said Yusuf.

'Last night each of us had a dream.' The man paused.

'Tell me your dreams and I will tell you what they mean', said Yusuf.

'I dreamt that I was in the King's vineyard,' said the first man. 'I had a wine-glass in my hand. I took some grapes and pressed the juice into the glass and gave it to the King.'

The prophet nodded and asked the other man about his dream.

'I dreamt I was carrying a basket of bread on my head. Suddenly a bird swooped down, took hold of the basket and flew off with it', said the man.

The men were anxious to hear the explanations of their dreams.

'I am the prophet of Allah', Yusuf began 'Allah has shown me the meaning of your dreams. The man who pressed juice from the grapes will be released from prison and go back to work in the palace.' The man smiled with relief. He had worked at the palace, in charge of the King's wine. When the King's enemies had asked him to poison the King, he had refused. He was innocent.

'The man with the basket will be punished and killed by order of the King, and birds will eat the flesh from his bones,' said the prophet. Yusuf was sorry for the man, who began to weep. But the man had been the King's baker and poisoned the King's food. The King had been warned and had not eaten it.

As the other man tried to comfort him, the prophet told them to accept the will of Allah. He explained to those who had come to listen that Allah controls the world but men are free to choose to live a good or a bad life.

A few days later the baker was killed and the other man freed. Yusuf became famous for his skill in explaining dreams.

The King's dream

The King woke with a start. He had had a strange and worrying dream. He sat up in the dark and thought about it. No one else was awake and the palace was very quiet.

In his dream seven fat cows had come out of the sea, followed by seven very thin cows. The seven thin cows had eaten up the seven fat cows but they didn't get any fatter.

The King thought about it for a while but he couldn't think what it meant. He lay down and went back to sleep.

Suddenly he woke up again. He jumped out of bed, shaking his head. He had had another strange dream. This time he had seen seven pieces of ripe wheat and seven dry, wilted pieces of wheat. And the dry pieces had taken the ripe wheat away.

'These dreams must be important', said the King to himself. 'They must mean something.'

As soon as the sun rose, the King called his astrologers and fortune-tellers and told them about his dreams. They were worried because they had never been called so early in the morning before. It must be something very serious, and the

King looked so severe. But none of them could understand what the dreams could mean.

The King let them go, but he was uneasy.

'If they cannot find the meaning of these dreams, it must be something very important indeed', he thought.

Everyone in the palace was talking about the mystery of the King's dreams. When the servant who was in charge of the King's wine heard about it, he remembered the prophet Yusuf in prison. He had been right about his dream.

So the servant hurried to the King and said, 'Forgive me, your majesty, but I know of a worthy young man in prison. He is very clever. He understands all the mysteries of the world. He can interpret dreams.'

The King looked up with interest at these words. He told the servant to go immediately to the prison and speak to the man.

The servant found Yusuf, still in the same cell.

'Forgive me for troubling you', he began, but the prophet smiled and asked him to go on.

The servant described the King's

dreams about the cows and the wheat.

'If you can work out the meaning of these dreams, the King and all his people will be very grateful to you', said the servant.

The prophet had listened quietly to the man's tale. He was not confused as the astrologers and fortune-tellers had been. Allah gave the prophet understanding and knowledge.

Yusuf explained that the seven fat cows and the ripe wheat meant seven good years for the people of Egypt. There would be peace, the people would be happy and there would be plenty to eat and drink. But then he explained that the seven thin cows and the dry wheat meant that the seven good years would be followed by seven bad years; years of drought and poor harvests.

The servant was astonished as he

listened to the meaning of the dreams.

'What will happen after that?' he asked.

'There will be peace and happiness again', said the prophet. 'There will be good harvests and the people will pick grapes to make wine and olives for their oil. They will be rich and well-fed.'

The servant was delighted at the prophet's words, then he remembered the seven bad years. The prophet understood his worries and said, 'If what I have said comes true, then remember this in the seven good years. Store as much food as you can for the bad years that will follow.'

The servant thanked Yusuf warmly and returned to the King.

The King was delighted to hear the secret of his dreams. But he asked the servant, 'Is what this man says true?'

'Yes, your majesty, I believe it is', replied the servant and he told the King about his own dream that Yusuf had explained correctly.

The King told his servant to go back to the prison and bring Yusuf to the palace.

When Yusuf heard the King's message, he told the servant that he was happy to go and see the King but he wanted the King to grant him a request first. He wanted the forty foolish women and Zulaiha to go to the King and tell him that he, Yusuf, was innocent.

The King agreed and sent for the women. Ashamed, they stood before the King and admitted that Yusuf had been treated unfairly. Zulaiha was sorry she had been so selfish and caused Yusuf to be sent to prison when he was innocent.

The King immediately gave orders for Yusuf's release. The servant went to give the prophet the good news.

So Yusuf left the prison after twelve years, full of memories of his experiences there.

At the door of the palace he prayed, 'Oh my God, I am part of your plan on this Earth. You are always with me. Only You are worthy to be worshipped.' Then he went into the palace.

The new minister

The prophet Yusuf entered the palace of the King of Egypt. As he walked to the Audience Chamber he prayed, 'Oh my God, I pray that good will come from this meeting with the King and I ask for Your protection from evil men.'

He was not afraid of the King. He knew there was no one greater than Allah and that the King of Egypt was just a man.

The King greeted him warmly. He was delighted to meet this man who had succeeded where his astrologers had failed. He welcomed him and invited him to sit down.

'Young man,' said the King, 'what do you think of my dream? What do you think should be done?'

The prophet replied, 'In my opinion your majesty should store as much grain as possible. The people should work as hard as they can in the fields and store the extra grain they produce in the good years in government granaries. The grain you store will be enough to feed all the people during the bad years – not only the people of Egypt but the people of neighbouring countries too. Foreign traders will come to Egypt to buy your grain and you will be praised for planning so well.'

The King thought about the prophet's plan carefully. It would need to be well organised. He could not think of any of his ministers who would be capable of the work. There was only one answer to the problem. He would ask the prophet Yusuf to take on the job.

'From what I know of your experience and knowledge, you are the only man who can carry out this plan. You are the only man worthy of the honour', said the King to Yusuf.

Yusuf accepted the responsibility willingly. The King was greatly relieved and appointed the prophet his minister for the welfare and economy of the country. This meant that he was the 'keeper of the treasures of the Earth'. The future not only of the people of Egypt but of many other people too depended on Yusuf. But Yusuf knew that all he did was due to the power of Allah. He told the King that only those who had faith in Allah would survive the bad years, when there would be no rain and the ground would be dry and bare.

The King listened carefully to Yusuf's plans. During the seven good years the people must be shown how to farm their land well. All the available land in Egypt must be used to grow food. The King felt happier as he pictured the wheat ripening in the fields.

Then Yusuf talked about his plans to build government granaries to store the grain and how he would organise the collection of the crops. The King nodded happily. He knew he had chosen the right man for the job.

'Yes, I understand your plans', said the King. 'I will order every government official and every citizen of Egypt to obey you.' He held out his hand in friendship to the prophet.

The King invited the prophet to dinner. As they ate they continued to discuss their plans for the future. They hoped the people of Egypt would not suffer too much during the difficult years.

The King was grateful to Yusuf but the prophet told him that the future was in Allah's hands. He explained that sometimes Allah used difficulties and hardship to test His servants but He would reward them with pleasure and rest. Hardship and ease, joy and sorrow were all part of Allah's plan for mankind. Only Allah could be asked for help.

The two brothers

Yahuza saw the caravan in the distance. He watched the travellers nervously as they came nearer. At last he recognised his brothers, but was Binyamin with them?

For two years there had been no rain and people were dying of hunger throughout the Arabian peninsula. When he heard there was food in Egypt, Ya'qub sent his sons to try and buy grain to save the family. Ten brothers had set out across the burning desert that separated Kan'an from Egypt. They had travelled for days but at last they arrived safely. They had bought grain from the minister of Egypt who controlled the country's supplies and were ready to return home. They had not recognised this grand minister as the brother, Yusuf, they had left in a well so many years before. But Yusuf had recognised them.

The minister had asked them about their home in Palestine. When the brothers said there was another son, Binyamin, at home, the minister had insisted they return home to fetch him. Yahuza was forced to stay in Egypt until the brothers kept

their promise and returned with Binyamin.

Yahuza counted the travellers over and over again. Only when they were very near was he certain there were ten people. He was saved! They had brought Binyamin. He smiled with relief.

The minister welcomed the brothers warmly.

'This is the brother we promised to bring back with us,' said Syam'un pushing Binyamin forward.

Yusuf was so happy to see his brother again and wanted to hug him, but he couldn't. He didn't want the others to know who he was yet.

'Thank you for keeping your promise,' said the minister, and he invited them to the dining hall.

The ten brothers sat down, leaving Binyamin on his own. The minister went up the boy.

'If my brother, Yusuf, was here, he would sit with me', said the unhappy boy. He told the minister about his brother and Yusuf longed to tell Binyamin who he was. He talked to Binyamin about his father and mother, then he invited the boy to sleep at his house that night.

When they were alone in his house, Yusuf told Binyamin that he was his brother. They hugged each other with joy as Binyamin said, 'My brother, I will never leave you again.' But they knew that Ya'qub would not let Binyamin stay in Eygpt. Ya'qub was still sad at the loss of his favourite son, Yusuf, and he loved Binyamin too much to let him go.

Yusuf thought of a plan. He would hide a cup in Binyamin's bag when the brothers set out for Palestine. The officials at the city gates would search their luggage and Binyamin would not be allowed to leave.

That night they both slept well.

Next morning Yusuf carried out his plan. The travellers were stopped at the city gates and, to the astonishment of his brothers, a cup was found in Binyamin's bag. The officials would not let Binyamin leave.

'Binyamin, what have you done?' his brothers cried. They were all scared at the thought of going home without him. They had promised their father to return Binyamin safe and sound. Again and again they asked the officials to let one of them stay in Binyamin's place but it was no good. The officials could not keep an innocent man and let a thief go free.

The ten brothers set out unhappily for Kan'an. They did not know how they could face their father without Binyamin. They knew his heart would break.

Father and son

The prophet Ya'qub was so sad. The sons he loved so much had been taken from him. Long ago he had wept over Yusuf's blood-stained clothes. Now Binyamin, too, was gone. His heart ached with unhappiness but at last his tears had stopped. He knew he must accept Allah's will without question and now he prayed to Allah to help him to be brave. He put his faith in Allah and repeated the names of Yusuf and Binyamin. Maybe, even now, Allah was protecting them.

Ya'qub was alone. His ten sons had returned to Egypt to look for Yusuf and Binyamin. His eyesight was poor now. Only Yusuf and Binyamin would relieve him of his sorrow.

After days of travelling across the burning desert, the exhausted brothers arrived once again in Egypt. They hoped that this time they could help their father. They knew they had done wrong when they left Yusuf in the well all those years ago. They wished they had looked after Binyamin better. They were sad when they thought of their father, lonely and unhappy in his old age.

They went to the palace to meet the minister again and told him how their family had suffered, especially their father, ever since Binyamin was accused of theft.

Yusuf was very sad on hearing the story. He held back his tears. He did not want them to know who he was just yet. He looked at his brothers and asked, 'Do you remember something you did long ago? You hated your brother so much that you tied him up and threw him into the well of Jub. You did this dreadful thing to your own brother.'

The brothers stared at him in surprise.

'But .. but ...' began one of them. He was trembling with shock ... 'But you must be Yusuf.' They were all so ashamed of what they had done.

'Yes, I am Yusuf. Allah has looked after me, and sent my brother, Binyamin, to me.'

None of the brothers knew what to say. They were so sad to remember what they had done to Yusuf, but they were happy, too, at the thought of taking such good news to their father. When he knew his sons were alive and safe, he would become strong and happy again. As they stood before Yusuf, they trembled with fear. They thought he would punish them. But the prophet was forgiving.

'I do not want to harm you', he said gently. 'Allah has forgiven you all your sins.'

They told him how unhappy their father had been. He was old and weak now, and almost blind.

The prophet was sad to hear about his father. He gave some of his clothes to Yahuza and told him to take them to his father as a sign, and bring Ya'qub back to Egypt.

They returned home once more. Yahuza gave Ya'qub the clothes, just as he had given him Yusuf's blood-stained clothes many years

before. Ya'qub recognised the scent of the clothes and knew his son was still alive. He prayed to Allah with joy and asked Him to forgive his sons for their cruelty. Then he set out with his family for Egypt where Yusuf was now a great and famous man. His dream of many years ago had come true.